Cornish Rocks and Minerals

Simon Camm

Alison Hodge

First published in 2010 by Alison Hodge,
2 Clarence Place, Penzance, Cornwall
TR18 2QA, www.alison-hodge.co.uk,
info@alison-hodge.co.uk

The right of Simon Camm to be identified as the
author of this work has been asserted by him
in accordance with the Copyright, Designs and
Patents Act 1988.

ISBN-13 978-0-906720-71-4

British Library Cataloguing-in-Publication Data
A catalogue record for this book is available from
the British Library.

Designed and originated by BDP – Book
Development & Production, Penzance, Cornwall

Printed in China

Title page: Connelite and botallackite, Levant

Acknowledgements

My special thanks goes to Ian Bruce of Crystal
Classics (www.crystalclassics.co.uk), who kindly
allowed me to use many of his company's
photographs of Cornish minerals. Thanks also
to Michael Merry of Cornwall Devon Mineral
Specimens (www.cornwalldevonmineralspeci-
mens.co.uk) for selected photographs taken
by him of the botallackite *in situ*, Wherry Mine
pump column and wolframite outcrop. Two
private collectors, one who wishes to remain
anonymous, and the other, Courtney Smale,
are thanked for access to their collections.

The image of the opal from St Austell is cred-
ited to Greenside Minerals (www.greensid-
eminerals.com). I am very grateful to Dr Sam
Weller for introducing me to Alison Hodge,
and for access to his collection. A thank you to
Sara Chambers, Collections Manager, the Royal
Cornwall Museum, Truro (www.royalcorn-
wallmuseum.org.uk), for permission to publish
images of several minerals held in the collections on display in the museum. Finally, a thank
you to Val, my wife, for waiting patiently for the
clouds to move so I could a take a photograph!

Contents

Introduction

As you explore the Cornish landscape, you will often see remnants of past, and in some cases more recent mining activity, in the form of engine houses with stacks or occasionally headgear, sometimes perched precariously on the edge of the cliffs. These are reminders of an activity which exploited Cornwall's rich geological resource of metalliferous minerals contained in the rocks underfoot.

The many elements sought or discovered were not only of tin and copper but also of lead, zinc, tungsten, antimony, silver, cobalt, nickel, uranium, bismuth, iron, manganese and molybdenum, and traces of gold and platinum. They also include the metalloid arsenic. This rich chemical suite is rarely found as native metals, but they are often combined with other elements to form different mineral species.

Cornwall's natural geological resources have been exploited since prehistoric times. Moor stones were used to build stone circles and, later, tombs. These are now scattered across the landscape, especially on high

Carn Galver and mines, West Penwith

Prehistoric stone circle, Nine Maidens, West Penwith (left). Alluvial cassiterite, Goss Moor, St Austell (above)

ground. Local material such as greenstone was used in the production of axes, which were often exported and used for trade in the neolithic period. Later, during the Bronze Age, man turned prospector, and hence mineral collector, for alluvial cassiterite (tin oxide), and most probably for copper ores for the production of bronze weapons and tools. Underground mining commenced in the Middle Ages, and reached its zenith in the nineteenth century, which included mining out under the sea for over 2.5 km.

It was during the eighteenth and nineteenth centuries that mineral collecting became a hobby of the landed gentry, and mineral dealers such as Lavin in the Egyptian House, Chapel Street, Penzance, set up in

Clockwise from top left: Underground at Rosevale Mine, Zennor, West Penwith; a poster for Lavin's shop, Penzance; liroconite, Wheal Gorland, St Day

the early 1800s to supply their needs. It is these specimens, collected during the heyday of Cornish mining, that form the basis of many of today's museum collections.

About this Book

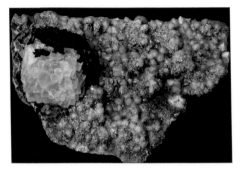 

Fluorite on amethyst, Wheal Jane, near Truro (left). Bornite, Carn Brea Mine, Redruth (right)

As a young boy, I looked into a grotto lined with crystals and metallic ores, and ever since, I have been fascinated by minerals. This enthusiasm was to lead to my profession as a geologist. Unless you specifically visit a museum, it is hard to appreciate the visual impact of such beautiful, colourful and aesthetically pleasing crystallized mineral specimens. Hopefully this book will give a greater awareness of this aspect of nature's wonders.

As minerals and rocks are inanimate objects, and often of subterranean origin, it is difficult to write about them without giving a little technical background. So this book introduces you to the basics of the county's geology, as well as to some of the processes of mineralization and the formation of minerals. Hopefully, this will increase your understanding and appreciation of how rocks and minerals are formed. Inevitably, there is some technical language, but I have provided a glossary and a little help with the physical properties of minerals (pages 110–11).

Cornwall, for its size, has one of the most diverse ranges of mineral species in the UK, if not the world. Many of these are spectacu-

Crowns engine house, Botallack, St Just, Penwith

lar in colour and crystal habit. Luckily for us today, others appreciated their beauty and form and collected them during the heyday of mining in the eighteenth and nineteenth centuries. These specimens are now found in museum collections such as those of the Royal Cornwall Museum in Truro and the Natural History Museum in London. Some local museums and private collectors have smaller collections.

Mine dumps, St Just, Penwith

Many minerals were discovered in the early days of mining, and the remains of this industrial activity have produced mining landscapes of such international prominence that in 2006 they were given World Heritage status by UNESCO. Some of the sites where certain minerals have been found have SSSI (Sites of Special Scientific Interest) status, and are protected against indiscriminate collecting. Others, of lesser importance but worth

Kilmar Tor, Twelve Mens Moor, Bodmin Moor (left).
Amethyst vein, St Just, West Penwith (above)

preserving or noting, have RIGS (Regional Important Geological Sites) status, and again collecting here is discouraged.

The rocks hosting the minerals cannot be ignored; these have produced the beautiful Cornish coastline and moorscapes that we see today. Their use as building materials has produced the local character of Cornish towns and villages. These native rocks were mined for religious reasons in prehistoric times, and quarried up to, and including, today for dimension stone and other house-building materials. Some of the more colourful varieties have been exploited for ornamental stone; others, of a softer character, have been carved into small objects. The granite rock, which forms the county's 'backbone', produced china clay when decomposed, and has been an important source of Cornwall's income during and since the decline of metalliferous mining.

To help you discover Cornwall's rich and diverse mineralogical heritage, I have divided the county into eleven districts, stretching from Land's End to the Tamar at the boundary with Devon. For each, there are approximately eight images of minerals found there, as well as two scenic views to give a flavour of the district. Such a plethora of wonderful minerals – each unique in form – has been found in the county that it is impossible to include all those found in each district. I have therefore included a gallery of minerals (pages 88–109) to illustrate the variety of form and colour (many images courtesy of **Crystal Classics Ltd**, **www.crystalclassics.co.uk**). Specimens illustrated here mostly range in size from 2 cm to 10 cm; those that are not in this range have their approximate size identified or noted if magnified. Additionally, I have included a few pages (85–7) on precious metals and semi-precious stones, and a section on the more common Cornish rocks (pages 78–84).

Unlike other aspects of nature in Cornwall, which can mostly be seen in the 'wild' at 'surface', the best examples of rocks and minerals are found in museum collections. The most colourful and attractive minerals occurred at a shallow depth, so many were recovered in the early days of underground mining. However, others are being formed today, in spoil heaps and underground. That does not detract from the fact that smaller and perhaps less dramatic examples can still be observed in the 'field', and can be found as outcrop, as pebbles on the beach, or as micro-specimens in non-protected mine dumps. These are best observed with a hand lens or microscope.

When walking this wonderful county, imagine the geological subterranean treasure trove under your feet, and the wonderful diversity of mineral species contained. If you wish to increase your knowledge, or to help preserve this heritage, you can join the Russell Society (www.russellsoc.org) for minerals, or RIGS (www.cornwallrigs.org.uk), which is dedicated to preserving Cornwall's geological diversity.

Note:
Cliffs and mine workings are dangerous, and you are not encouraged to visit these sites. Many workings are on private property, and many are protected sites where collecting is not permitted.

Geology and Mineralization

Cornwall's diverse scenery is a direct result of the underlying geology. The major rock forming Cornwall is of sedimentary origin, derived from silts and sands eroded from highlands onshore and deposited in marine basins during the Devonian to Carboniferous periods some 400 to 200 million years ago. Undersea volcanic activity during this time produced basaltic rocks which now form prominent headlands due to their resistance to erosion. As the molten lava extruded into the cold sea it formed pillows, and where these intruded into the sediments they became thick, flat-lying bodies which were later exploited by quarrying for road stone. Due to the movement of plate tectonics, the sediments were folded; spectacular examples of this are exposed in North Cornwall. It was during this period of mountain-building, or orogeny, that hot granite magma was intruded from below to form a backbone to the county, called a batholith, running on into Dartmoor in Devon. Granite is formed from the minerals of quartz, feldspar and mica.

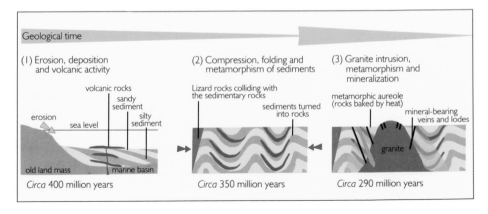

Geological time

(1) Erosion, deposition and volcanic activity

volcanic rocks
sandy sediment
silty sediment
erosion
sea level
old land mass
marine basin

Circa 400 million years

(2) Compression, folding and metamorphism of sediments

Lizard rocks colliding with the sedimentary rocks
sediments turned into rocks

Circa 350 million years

(3) Granite intrusion, metamorphism and mineralization

metamorphic aureole (rocks baked by heat)
mineral-bearing veins and lodes
granite

Circa 290 million years

Volcanic pillow lavas, Clodgy Point, St Ives, West Penwith (left). Folding of sedimentary rocks, Crackington Haven, near Bude, North Cornwall (right)

At and near the intrusion of the hot granite, the country rocks of shales and volcanics were 'baked' or metamorphosed into hard rocks forming a metamorphic aureole around the intrusion.

Due to erosion over geological time the granite core, where it formed high spots, has been exposed to form the castellated granite cliffs and exposed tors on the high ground inland that are such a feature of Cornwall. Near the end of the granite intrusion, another granitoid rock of feldspar and quartz, known locally as elvan dykes, intruded as sub-vertical sheets.

Again due to plate tectonic movement, a sliver of the ocean floor was forced up against these rocks to form the Lizard complex. This rare suite of rocks has produced not only the serpentine for which it is famous. It also exposed other rocks that form the boundary between the lithosphere (the crust and upper mantle) and mantle which only occur deep in the earth's crust, where the plates are spreading apart in the deep ocean.

During the intrusion of the granite magma, the heat produced a circulation of water. This hot water, or hydrothermal activity, leached metallic elements from the surrounding rock

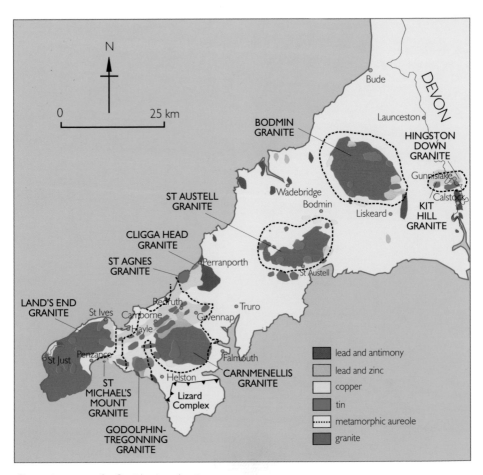

Emanative centres for Cornish mineralization

Granite, Treryn Dinas from Porthcurno beach, West Penwith

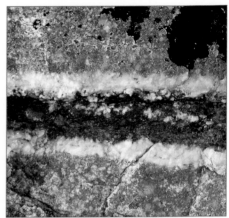

Serpentine, Kennack Sands, the Lizard (left). Mineral vein, St Micheael's Mount, Mount's Bay (right)

and granite and focused them into fractures or faults. As the mineralized solutions rose upwards, and due to a release in pressure, cooling and change in chemistry lead to the deposition of minerals, including metalliferous ones, to form ore bodies, or ore deposits of veins known locally as lodes. A simplistic view of these mineral deposits is one where there is zoning from high-temperature minerals, such as cassiterite and wolframite, occurring in or very near the granite with copper near-by, and low-temperature ones, such as zinc and lead, much further away.

As the heat decreased over time, it caused the decay of the mineral-bearing waters, and a change of direction of the source rocks of the metals. This lead to an overprinting of the more high-temperature mineralization formed earlier in geological time, and also new low-temperature ore deposits such as lead and antimony. The mineralization formed by all these processes formed the world-famous Cornubian Ore Field, which stretches from Land's End into Devonshire.

A mineral vein, or lode (facing page)

MINERAL VEIN OR LODE

ZONE AND MINERALS

PRESENT LAND SURFACE

CRYSTALLIZATION

GOSSAN ZONE
quartz/iron oxides

(quartz, limonite, goethite,
haematite, cassiterite, +/-gold)

SUPERGENE ZONE
arsenates/chlorides/carbonates/
sulphates, phosphates, oxides/native metal
and secondary sulphides

(malachite, azurite, olivenite, clinoclase,
pharmochosiderite, scorodite, liroconite,
chalcophyllite, pyromorphite, mimetite,
cuprite, native copper, bornite, chalcocite, etc.)

SULPHIDE ZONE
primary sulphides

(quartz, chalcopyrite, arsenopyrite,
löllengite, with cassiterite)

TIN ZONE
(quartz, chlorite, tourmaline, cassiterite)

cassiterite and quartz

cassiterite and quartz

cassiterite and quartz

cassiterite/ quartz

cassiterite/ quartz

cassiterite/ quartz

cassiterite/ quartz

cassiterite/ quartz

cassiterite/ quartz

SOMETIMES CRYSTALLIZED
(area sometimes called 'Iron Hat')

present water table c. 30 m

OFTEN WELL CRYSTALLIZED
(area of beautiful and colourful secondary minerals)

old water table c. 100 m

OCCASIONALLY WELL CRYSTALLIZED
(area of primary ore minerals)

Iron oxides and cassiterite

Gold and quartz

Limonite

Liroconite and clinoclase

Chalcophyllite

Scorodite

Across these two pages, from top left to bottom right, are examples of Cornish minerals that may be encountered with increasing depth in a mineral lode or vein

Much later in geological time, during a period of subtropical weathering, these lodes were subjected to the leaching of metals by the downward movement of acidic surface waters. Complex electrochemical processes at the water table, and variations in the water table,

Cuprite

Native copper

Chalcocite

Chalcopyrite

Arsenopyrite

Cassiterite

produced the beautiful crystallized, sometimes rare minerals, seen in collections today.

This process left a brown, iron-rich top, often with cassiterite and quartz, known as 'iron hat' or gossan. It was the first area to be exploited by miners for the rich and simple tin ore, possibly in prehistoric times, and certainly in the Middle Ages.

Below the brown gossan, colourful carbonates, arsenates and phosphates formed, beneath which lay very rich secondary copper ores of native oxides and sulphides of copper.

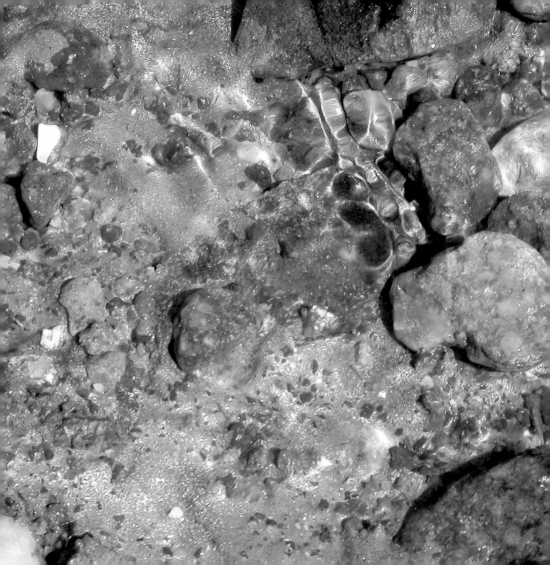

*Botallackite mineral growing in situ today in a
pool near Perranporth (left). Botallackite crystals,
(magnified, above)*

This shallow but rich copper ore produced
great wealth during the Cornish copper-
mining boom in the eighteenth and early
nineteenth centuries. Under all lie the primary ores of sulphides with cassiterite that
were mined almost up to the end of the
twentieth century.

The process of forming new minerals
is continuing today, both on mining waste
dumps – due to the oxidation of minerals because of the downward movement of water
in them – and in old abandoned mine workings, especially where mineralized water
meets and often reacts with seawater.

West Penwith: St Just to St Ives

Native copper, Botallack, near St Just (left). Chalcocite, St Ives Consols, St Ives (right)

The north-coast area of the district of Penwith covers the famous ore field of St Just to Pendeen, including the world-famous Botallack and Levant mines which exploited ores well out under the sea, and extending to the picturesque seaside resort of St Ives. Inland, the area of higher ground is bleak moorland, with many prehistoric monuments; this tumbles abruptly into a flat coastal strip of farmland, with small fields and villages before the cliffs above the sea. Most mining activity took place near the cliff edge, which, in the case of the Crowns engine shaft (photo page 10), led to mine buildings perched precipitously just above the high-water line. This coastal strip with its cliff-side mines, is well known and one in particular, Botallack, is well described in R.M. Ballantyne's romantic novel *Deep Down*, published in the 1800s. This part of Penwith is renowned for its diversity of metallic ores of tin, copper, uranium, bismuth, lead and zinc, as well as rare species of minerals such as botallackite, a blue-green copper chloride, and stokesite, a very rare tin

Kenidjack Valley looking towards Cape Cornwall

mineral, which were first found in the district. The area is littered with derelict mine buildings and dumps of waste rocks discarded by past mining activity. Geevor, Levant and St Ives Consols mines are known for their very fine crystallized specimens of grey chalcocite, an ore of copper, as well as native copper at Botallack Mine and silvery-white metallic native bismuth at St Ives Consols. Around St Just, fine purple amethyst specimens were

Rosewall Hill looking towards St Ives

recovered from underground in the past, and more recently from the mine dumps.

Initially mined for copper, many of the mines produced tin in depth as they approached and entered the granite. Near Botallack, the sliver of country rocks or slates and volcanic greenstones follows the coast with the granite just inland. Here silicate minerals such as axinite and garnets, as well as the magnetic iron mineral magnetite, outcrop on the cliffs. Taking a compass here will illustrate the magnetic forces at work where the magnetite outcrops reach the surface in certain areas. Uranium ores also occur on this coast, for instance at Wheal Edward Mine near St Just, which was re-examined in the 1950s by the UK Atomic Agency as a potential source of uranium ore. Here, as

Clockwise from top left: Axinite, Botallack, near St Just; atacamite, Levant Mine, Pendeen; amethyst, Carn Gloose, St Just; erythrite, Botallack Mine

well as pitchblende – an ore of uranium – very colourful 'fluorescent' uranium secondary minerals of green and yellow have been uncovered. At St Ives, at Wheal Trenwith, the dumps were picked over in the 1900s for pitchblende, not only as a yellow-green colourant for glass, but also later for Madame Curie to recover radium. The area has

Clockwise from top left: Zippeite, Wheal Edward, St Just; calcite, Geevor Mine, Pendeen; limonite, Wheal Owles, St Just; native bismuth, St Ives Consols, St Ives

a long history of mining, and Geevor Mine near Pendeen, now a fine museum, only ceased production in the latter part of the twentieth century.

Mount's Bay: Penzance to Porthleven

Mount's Bay

The coastal strip from Newlyn near Penzance to Loe Bar near Porthleven includes the tiny island of St Michael's Mount, which dominates most of the vistas. Near Newlyn lies the Wherry Mine, so named after the flat-bottomed boats that operated from the shingle nearby. This was a truly submarine mine. Initially, the tin-bearing elvan rock was exploited at low tide some 200 metres offshore; later, a shaft was sunk with a collar to keep out the seawater, to exploit the ore below. This was undertaken in the

Wherry Mine, Penzance (above), and cassiterite vein in elvan from the mine (below)

eighteenth century, and at first was a great financial success. All that is left to remind us of this extraordinary venture is the pump column when exposed at low spring tides. Ore specimens of the elvan, with impregnations and veins of cassiterite, can still be found by carefully searching the storm beach above high water below Penzance promenade.

A little to the north-east, at Marazion beach, the shingle can turn up colourful pebbles,

Pebbles on Marazion beach

St Michael's Mount (above). Greisen vein with wolframite in a boulder, St Michael's Mount (below)

of agate, carnelian and porphyry. Further along the beach and near the harbour at St Michael's Mount, granite cobbles with mineralized veins containing wolframite and cassiterite can be found by careful examination of the foreshore. St Michael's Mount comprises a small granite cupola, shrouded by metamorphosed sediments with only the seaward edge of granite exposed. Here in the granite are multiple veins containing cassiterite,

Clockwise from top left: Cobble with sulphides of copper, zinc and lead, Perranuthnoe; apatite on feldspar, Tremearne, near Porthleven; pyromorphite, Wheal Rose, Porthleven

Along the coast at Perranuthnoe, the beach can furnish specimens of lead and zinc ores as well as copper sulphide, these being derived either from mineral lodes offshore, or from mine debris deposited on the beach. Chalcopyrite has a golden colour; sphalerite is black and shiny, and galena silver-white when fresh but lead-grey when oxidized. Going south-east is another granite outcrop, from Praa Sands to Tremearne cliff, which includes Rinsey Cove where pegmatites are exposed. Wonderful examples of blue to purple apatite crystals have been discovered here, and occasionally rare topaz.

wolframite, topaz, apatite and even beryl. However, the site is private and an SSSI, and collecting is not permitted.

Loe Pool

Between Porthleven and Loe Bar, lead lodes with the rare lead chloride mineral phosgenite can be exposed after a storm at low tide; just inland on the same lodes in the mines, beautiful bright green pyromorphite was once discovered. Further along the beach at Loe Bar, the shingle can throw up interesting colourful pebbles of quartz and serpentine, as well as flint and chert from geological deposits lying offshore or further up the coast, and specimens of the lead lodes just to the north-west.

Note:
The beach at Loe Bar can be extremely dangerous at all states of the tide, especially with heavy seas running.

Phosgenite (magnified), Porthleven

Rivers Hayle to Cober:
Hayle to Helston

Hayle Estuary looking towards Hayle Towans

Hayle is situated on the estuary or confluence of the River Hayle and a small river to the east running down from Angarrack. The town was a port for many years, serving the mining industry, and was a major smelting town for both tin and copper. The estuary has silted up, and is now a sanctuary for birds.

The area extends from Hayle to Helston, an ancient borough town to the south-east on the River Cober. Here, as at Hayle, over time the estuary silted up from mine-waste sediments discharged into the water courses. The upper reaches of the old estuary are now covered in wetland vegetation, and at

Clockwise from top left: Pyromorphite, Wheal Alfred, Hayle; native silver, Wheal Herland, Gwinear; bayldonite, Penberthy Croft, St Hilary; malachite, Wheal Carpenter, near Leedstown

the seaward end is a freshwater lake behind a shingle bar. This belt of mineralized ground between the two towns yielded copper and tin as well as large tonnages of lead con-taining silver. In part the area is constrained by the distinctive outline of the Godolphin-Tregonning granite, and to the east the higher ground of Carnmenellis granite. Tin in the

Wheal Pool Mine, Helston

and copper minerals, a small deposit of native silver was uncovered at Wheal Herland Mine in the form of masses of silver 'wires'. On the Wheal Alfred Road before Fraddom lies the Wheal Carpenter Mine, well known for the occurrence of apple- to dark-green-coloured rare copper lead arsenate, bayldonite, dark green copper phosphate pseudomalachite, and the green copper carbonate, malachite, as well as other rare mineral species.

Near Leedstown, the copper-rich Crenver and Abraham mines produced spectacular crystallized specimens of the grey copper mineral chalcocite. Rare copper and lead arsenate minerals occurred towards St Hilary at Penberthy Croft Mine, where a whole suite of unusual, colourful and sometimes rare lead arsenate minerals have been found. These include bayldonite, and the sky-blue lead-copper sulphate mineral linarite, and many others have been recorded by mineralogists. Other minerals found include the white iron arsenate mineral liskeardite and, unusually, the tungsten mineral scheelite.

Near Carleen, north-west of Helston, lie the very rich tin mines of Wheal Vor, and opencast mine of Wheal Fortune, where occasionally cassiterite specimens may still be found on mine waste tips.

form of cassiterite has been plentiful near and in the granite, with copper and lead production further away.

Near Hayle, Wheal Alfred, a lead mine, produced beautiful crystallized specimens of yellow-green pyromorphite, an arsenate of lead, the finest found in Cornwall. Just to the north of this mine at Gwinear, as well as tin

Clockwise from top left: Mimetite, Penberthy Croft, St Hilary; pyromorphite, Wheal Pool, Helston; chalcocite, Crenver and Abraham Mine, Leedstown; cassiterite, Wheal Lovel, near Helston

In the valley just south of Helston, some spectacular specimens of pyromorphite were recovered at the ancient Pool Mine, which exploited a silver-rich lead lode. To the north-west of the town, in the granite at Wendron, large crystals of cassiterite have occurred in some of the lodes at particular mines.

Camborne–Redruth:
Troon to Treleigh

Carn Brea Monument

Engine houses on the Great Flat Lode, near Carn Brea

One of the most famous mining districts in the world, the Camborne–Redruth tin and copper ore field has been mined intensively, probably in prehistory, and up to the end of the twentieth century. Its heyday was in the nineteenth century, when the district was littered with mines working side by side, especially over a large area on the western flank of Carn Brea Hill. Many mining artefacts and buildings can be seen in the district, from the King Edward Mine Museum near Troon to the National Trust's engine houses at Pool. Centred in the area is the monument to the Basset family at the top of Carn Brea granite hill, which dominates the district with a com-

manding view of the minescape to the north and south.

To the north-west of Carn Brea, the headgear of South Crofty Mine is visible. Exploratory mining is still taking place here at Cornwall's last surviving mine. Nearby lies the famous Dolcoath Mine, which in the nineteenth century, at just over 1,000 metres, was the deepest mine in the world. Predominantly a copper, and later a tin mine, it also produced a little silver and bismuth ores.

Just to the east of Carn Brea, between it and the granite hill above Carnkie, lies a 'saddle' of metamorphic rocks containing the Great Flat Lode, which runs for some

Clockwise from top left: Chalcocite, Redruth; bornite, Carn Brea Mine; blister copper, Dolcoath Mine; chalcopyrite, Carn Brea Mine

5 km, and at the end of the nineteenth century supported many mines along its path. Tin was exploited from gossans in the very early days of working, quickly followed by rich secondary copper deposits just below. These produced an interesting assemblage of secondary copper sulphide minerals, such as chalcocite and bornite, often well crystal-

Clockwise from top left: Fluorite, East Pool Mine; metatorbernite, Wheal Basset, Carnkie; fluorite, Carn Brea Mine; siderite, Tin Croft Mine

lized. Secondary minerals of arsenates and phosphates of copper occurred above, and at depth lay deposits of tin. Fine specimens

Dolcoath Mine, looking towards Carn Brea Hill (left). Bassetite, Wheal Basset (right)

of chalcopyrite were also recovered, and the crystallized form of cassiterite known as 'sparable tin', named because the crystals resembled sparrows' bills! As well as fine specimens of tin and copper minerals, the lodes contained fluorspar; very attractive specimens of this coloured cubic mineral have found their way into many collections, displaying their various forms of green, through yellow to purple. Well crystallized iron carbonate, known as siderite, also existed.

Bismuth, antimony and uranium occur in the district, as well as cobalt minerals. At Wheal Basset a yellow uranium mineral was named bassetite after that mine, and fine specimens of the green uranium mineral torbenite, from the same area, are displayed in many museums. Cobalt was exploited commercially at Wheal Sparnon, Redruth, for a blue colourant for pottery glazes, and an example of a blue-glazed plate and the ore from this mine are exhibited at the Royal Cornwall Museum in Truro. The mineral cobaltite, often covered in the pink cobalt secondary mineral erythrite, was the main source of cobalt ore at this mine.

Gwennap:
Carharrack to Carnon Downs

Gwennap Pit, an amphitheatre where John Wesley preached, is probably an old open-pit mine working

Copper arsenates liroconite (left) and chalcophyllite (right), both from Wheal Gorland

East of Camborne–Redruth, the Gwennap district includes Carharrack and St Day, and extends from the foot of the Carn Marth granite hill to the west, almost as far as Truro, and to Carnon Downs to the east. Metallic minerals found here range from copper, tin, zinc and silver-rich lead with minor tungsten, to gold and uranium, and often arsenic. One valley here is testament to the toxicity of the mine waste, supporting little or very stunted vegetation, which results in a desolate minescape. The area is covered with old mine spoil tips and mining artefacts. The valley below Bissoe, infilled with mine-waste products, extends down to the beautiful tidal area of Restronguet Creek below Carnon Downs.

Unity Wood Mine

This area was once the richest copper producer in the world. It is most famous for its spectacular coloured copper arsenate minerals, such as liroconite, clinoclase, olivenite and chalcophyllite, some of which are the best in the world. Other minerals include the arsenates of iron, such as the green cubes of pharmocosiderite, and blue-grey scorodite. Nearby, the orange-brown lead arsenate mimetite was discovered. Many other rare to very rare arsenates have been recorded from these mines. Additionally, superb specimens of native copper and cuprite occurred just below the colourful arsenates in the mines,

and were also recovered as specimens for early mineral collectors. They came primarily from the mines of Wheal Muttrell, Wheal Gorland, Wheal Unity, Wheal Jewel and Ting Tang. The blue copper carbonate azurite was reported at both Wheal Gorland and Ting Tang. Little now remains of their workings, apart from some small, desolate soil heaps.

The district also encompasses the Carnon Valley, where substantial placer or alluvial cassiterite was recovered from the valley bottom as the river drained the rich mining district of Gwennap. Placer mining (the mining of alluvial, usually water-borne, deposits for miner-

Clockwise from top left: Olivenite, Wheal Gorland; pharmacosiderite, Wheal Gorland; cuprite and native copper, Wheal Jewel; mimetite, Unity Wood Mine

als) extended well below sea level, with one remarkable mine employing underground mining methods in the alluvium for this ore in Restronguet. It was also well known for placer gold occurring with the cassiterite, and an 1808 find included the largest nugget discovered in Cornwall, which is now displayed at the Royal Cornwall Museum in Truro.

Ludlamite, Wheal Jane Mine (above). Azurite, Ting Tang Mine (right)

To the east lies Jane Mine – in the 1970s, Europe's most modern tin mine, when it reopened an old mine. It operated until the latter part of the twentieth century. Here cassiterite was the primary mineral mined, but in depth increasing amounts of zinc in the form of the mineral sphalerite were recovered for sale. The mine is famous for phosphates of iron, including the green-coloured ludlamite and brown cronstedite. Modern mining also exposed amethystine quartz crystals, with occasional large green fluorite crystals perched on them. Wheal Jane is unusual in that being a tin mine it is some distance from the granite at Carn Marth. Lying in the Wheal Jane sett, towards the east at Wheal Andrew, at one time beautiful specimens of crystallized barite and chalcopyrite in the form of 'blister copper' (named for its appearance) were found.

North Coast: Porthtowan to Perranporth

Chalcopyrite, South Wheal Towan, Porthtowan (left). Cassiterite, pseudomorph, Wheal Coates, St Agnes (right)

A coastal strip of mining activity where tin, copper, lead, zinc and iron were mined in the past extends from Porthtowan to Perranporth. Copper mining was predominant near Porthtowan, where spectacular crystallized chalcopyrite was occasionally found in the mines. Further along the coast, tin mining was the major activity, with lead and zinc inland. Most of the deposits lie in metamorphosed sedimentary rocks, but granite lies just under St Agnes Beacon and outcrops again at Cligga Head.

Picturesque Wheal Coates, perched on the edge of the cliff, is a much-photographed mining location. Here there was a most unusual occurrence of pseudomorphs, for which the mine is most famous. Cassiterite – that is tin oxide, the ore of tin – replaces feldspar crystals in the granite and takes on the shape of the previous mineral. Further along

Wheal Coates, St Agnes

the coast at Trevaunance Cove, the many tunnels of adits and excavations from previous mining are exposed in the cliffs. These, together with the numerous engine houses which can be seen are testament to intensive mining in the past. This area was very rich in tin ore, which can still be found among the pebbles on the beach after a storm. Many beautiful crystallized cassiterite specimens now grace mineral collections world-wide, as

Pebble with brown cassiterite, Trevaunance Cove, St Agnes (above). Cligga Head, near Perranporth (right)

well as those of crystallized pyrite and fluorite from the same locality. In the same vicinity is the celebrated form of cassiterite known as 'wood tin', so-called because of its banded appearance which resembles the rings of a tree. Specimens of this were found mainly at Wheal Kitty, and occasionally it can be found on the beach below.

Along the coast and before Perranporth lies the renowned outcrop of the Cligga Head granite headland, multi-coloured with red and green from iron and copper staining, and with widespread mineral veining. This

Clockwise from top left: Cassiterite, Trevaunance Mine, St Agnes; pyrite, Wheal Kitty, St Agnes; galena pseudomorphs after pyromorphite, Wheal Hope; chalcanthite, Perran St George Mine, Perranporth

too shows extensive mining, with numerous tunnels exposed in the cliff side. Here both cassiterite and tungsten, in the form of the mineral wolframite, were mined up to and during the Second World War, as tungsten is used in hardening steel. The silver-coloured minerals arsenopyrite, arsenic iron sulphide and loellingite (iron arsenide), occur in this

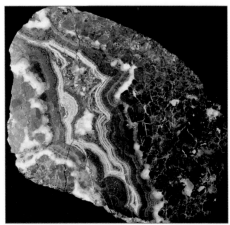

Vein of quartz and wolframite, Cligga Head (left). Wood tin, Wheal Kitty, St Agnes (right)

mine, and the greenish-silver stannite, a sulphide of tin, copper and iron, much derided by miners as it had no commercial value. The spoil tips here occasionally yield up specimens of these minerals, as well as the rare, soft yellow-brown secondary mineral of tin known as varlamoffite, and green iron arsenates of scorodite and pharmocosiderite.

In the cliff near Perranporth Beach both tin and copper were exploited by past mining, and very colourful secondary minerals such as chalcanthite, a copper sulphate, were found, as well as the mineral botallackite, a copper chloride, in recent times. These minerals are still forming today. Inland from Perranporth, at Wheal Hope, curious specimens of galena were obtained in the 1800s, after the secondary lead mineral pyromorphite. At the end of Perranporth beach, to the north-east, lies the entrance to an iron mine, Gravel Hill Mine, worked in the Second World War for the iron oxides of haematite and limonite, as well as the iron carbonate siderite. In recent times, unusual iron minerals have been discovered here. This iron lode, many metres wide, extends for several kilometres inland.

The Lizard: Mullion to Manaccan

Goonhilly Downs

Varoius coloured pebbles on Poltesco beach (left), and a hand-polished cobble of serpentine (right)

The Lizard district is quite individual: the topography is flat and the soils are mostly poor where the serpentine outcrops, with a distinctive and sometimes rare flora. The area extends from Mullion, on the south-west of heath land, around the coast to the wooded Helford River Estuary to the north, and on to the village of Manaccan to the north-east. The rock types found here are also unusual, forming a suite known as an ophilite complex – a section of oceanic crust rarely exposed at surface. The Lizard serpentine is the largest outcrop of this rock type in mainland Britain.

As the name the Lizard implies, there are multicoloured rocks of serpentine resembling a snake's skin. These have been quarried for material to turn into ornaments, especially in the Victorian period when such items were fashionable. Beautiful examples of serpentine, in the form of sea-polished cobbles, can be found on many of the beaches. Emery paper and a finish with a metal polish can achieve a similar polished surface to that of the manu-factured artefact. On the Lizard too there has been mineralization. The serpentine, for which it is famous, is the result of hot water changing the chemistry and producing new minerals from dark, igneous volcanic rocks.

Poltesco beach

During the geological period, when deep weathering took place, solutions from below and above lead to the deposition of native copper and the copper oxide of red cuprite with, occasionally, a fringe of native silver.

Small-scale mining for native copper has taken place. The deposits were very erratic in nature, but when found were extremely rich, being almost pure copper metal. There is still evidence of past mining activity, in the

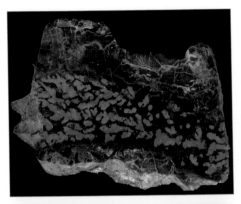

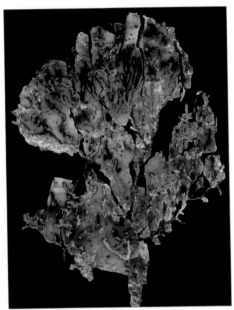

Clockwise from top left: Cuprite and native copper in serpentine; native copper dendrites in serpentine; zeolite, analcite

small workings in the form of tunnels exposed along certain cliffs. It is possible that this source of copper was exploited by prehistoric man in the Bronze Age, after the discovery of green-coloured 'lumps' on the surface or at cliff sites.

The area is also famed for the suite of well-crystallized zeolite aluminosilicate minerals such as analcine, natrolite and prehnite, as well as chalcedony, a variety of quartz, which was found in the past in one of the quarries. A trace of platinum has been discovered in

Clockwise from top left: Zeolite, natrolite; chalcedony and quartz; precious serpentine; asbestos vein

some of the ultrabasic rocks on the Lizard, and gold is reported in some of the streams. Illmenite, a black mineral of titanium, is found in abundance in some of the streams on the Lizard. It was first recognized and identified by the Revd William Gregor in 1791 at Manaccan, and he named it manaccanite after that village.

St Austell: Ladock to Lostwithiel

Nickeline, St Austell Consols, St Stephen (left). Smokey quartz, clay pit, St Austell (right)

The St Austell district covers a large area encompassing the St Austell granite, a topographic high, world-famous for its large opencast china clay, or kaolin, mines, and the surrounding country rocks of mainly shales and slates, both to the north and down to the coast, and from Ladock to Lostwithiel. The area has been extensively mineralized, and in the past produced tin, copper, tungsten and uranium, as well as gold from the streams draining the western end of the granite, as a byproduct of alluvial tin mining. There were also substantial tonnages of china clay, the mining of which continues today.

Around the periphery of the granite, on the western side the St Austell Consols Mine produced not only copper and tin but, unusually, nickel and cobalt ores, as well as uranium. The pale, copper-red nickel ore of nickeline, a nickel arsenide, is often covered

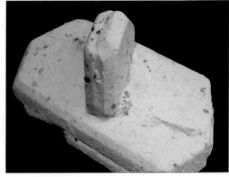

Apatite with quartz, Gunheath Pit, St Austell (magnified, left). 'Pig's egg', china clay pit, St Austell (right). China clay waste tip (facing page)

with the green secondary nickel mineral annabergite. Not far away lies South Terras Mine which, in the latter years of its life, produced uranium ores for glass-colouring and, later, radium recovery, for which a reclamation plant was set up. Rare uranium mineral species have been recorded from this mine, as well as the more common green secondary mineral torbernite, known locally as 'Green Jim'.

Many streams and rivers on the south-west side of the St Austell granite were renowned for carrying gold in the alluvial material in valley bottoms. One in particular is the Ladock Valley, which produced enough to make gold

jewellery, now on display in the Royal Cornwall Museum at Truro. It is assumed that the gossans from copper ore bodies, now mostly eroded, may have been one of the original sources for the gold found in the district.

The opencast clay pits in the centre of the granite have produced wonderful specimens of crystallized quartz, mainly white but occasionally black cairngorm and purple amethyst. Odd white crystals, known locally as 'pigs' eggs', were found in certain clay pits; these were replacements of feldspar crystals by sericite and kaolin.

In one area on the St Austell granite, at Trelavour Downs, brownish-purple, lithium-

Clockwise from top left: Turquoise, Gunheath Pit, St Austell; chalcotrichite, Fowey Consols Mine, Tywardreath; siderite, Wheal Maudlin Mine, Lanlivery; limonite, Restormel Royal Mine, Lanlivery

rich mica was mined. Mica cleaves readily into large flakes. This location must be the only known mica mine in the British Isles. Small but beautiful crystals of apatite, a calcium phosphate mineral, were found in one of the pits. Unusual, green-coloured phosphates of copper, secondary uranium minerals and coarsely crystallized cassiterite have also been recovered from the workings, as well as blue turquoise and opal.

On the south-eastern side of the granite, in country rocks, the mine known as Fowey Consols produced superb specimens of the carmine-red copper oxide mineral chalcotrichite, as well as the silvery bismuth sulphide mineral bismuthinite.

On the eastern side, at Wheal Maudlin Mine, exceptional crystallized specimens of the iron carbonate mineral siderite were uncovered by mining. This was nicknamed 'horse tooth spar', because of its unusual crystallized form, which, as its name implies, resembles the teeth of a horse.

Just north of Lostwithiel lies Restormel Royal Iron Mine, which started working in the late 1700s, and was famed for producing fine crystallized specimens of the black iron mineral goethite. This mine is also known for iron ore haematite specimens, as well as ores of manganese. On the northern side, in a small granite cupola, just exposed at surface and crowned by an Iron Age fort, Castle-an-Dinas, lie the remains of Cornwall's only tungsten mine, which only ceased mining the tungsten ore wolframite in the late 1950s.

Cassiterite vein in granite, clay pit, St Austell (top). Cassiterite, Old Beam Mine, St Austell (above)

Wadebridge:
Padstow to Port Gaverne

The Camel Estuary, looking seawards towards Stepper Point

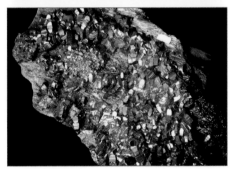

Clockwise from top left: Jamesonite, Treore Mine, near Port Isaac; stibnite, Wheal Boys Mine, St Endellion; bournonite, Wheal Boys Mine, St Endellion

The Wadebridge area is unusual for Cornwall, containing sporadic mineralization in the form of lead and antimony ores, often including zinc. The district runs from Padstow to Port Gaverne, just past Port Isaac, and inland to Wadebridge. The landscape is gently undulating, with occasional lightly wooded incised valleys to the sea. The biggest valley, now drowned, is the Camel Estuary, which runs up to Wadebridge, at what was the lowest crossing point. The estuary has the promontories of Pentire Point on the east and Stepper Point on the west, at the seaward end. Most of the mining activity was small, and the remains are now hard to find because it took place in the seventeenth and early eighteenth centuries. Antimony ores were first recovered for the production of pewter plate when mixed with lead. Later, antimony was used in the emerging chemical industry.

Most of the antimony ore was in the form of the silver-grey minerals jamesonite and stibnite. There was also occasional bournonite,

Clockwise from top left: Calcite, Port Quin Mine, Port Quin; pyromorphite, Trevinnick Mine, St Kew; cerrusite, Pentire Glaze Mine, St Minver

named after Count de Bournon who visited Wheal Boys mine, near Bodannon, St Endellion, in the very early 1800s. The mine remains noteworthy today for the crystallized specimens of this mineral associated with the dark brown zinc sulphide mineral sphalerite. Small outcrops of antimony and lead ores were also exploited by cliff-mining, evidence of which may be seen today. One spectacular part of an outcrop is on Port Quin beach, where the lode is exposed in a cave. This mine also produced wonderful delicate white calcite specimens. Lead ores were worked at Trevinnick Mine, in the Parish of St Kew, where fine specimens of the green lead secondary mineral, pyromorphite, have been recovered by mineral collectors in recent years.

Within the district lies the very old lead mine, Pentire Glaze, which was worked prior to the eighteenth century. Remains now are somewhat indistinct, with past waste dumps merging into the landscape on the headland

Port Quin Cove looking towards Pentire Head

of Pentire Point near Polzeath. This mine is prominent because superbly crystallized, very delicate specimens of a lead carbonate mineral, cerussite, were extracted from it. These specimens took the form of snow-white, thin interlocking crystals, which were given the name of 'Jack straws', because of their resemblance to straws of wheat. They were much sought after by the mineral collectors of the day, but due to their fragility had to be transported extremely cautiously. The antimony ores of the district are auriferous (gold-bearing), and many of the streams carry minor particles of gold in the alluvial sediments. In the history of Cornwall, one operation is unique in that it was set up in the First World War to recover gold from the alluvium in the stream draining into the cove at Port Gaverne. It was not a financial success!

Liskeard: Landreath to Linkinhorne

Phoenix Mine, near the Cheesewring

The Liskeard district extends from the major mining district around the granite country of the old mining village of Minions and Caradon Hill at Linkinhorne, down to near St Ive

on the south-east flank of the Bodmin granite. It covers the area south-west of Liskeard, including Herodsfoot in Landreath. The high, rugged, granite, heath-covered hinterland drops down to deep, wooded valleys running to the coast in the surrounding country rocks. Many of the mine waste dumps and associated mine buildings are still visible on the higher ground. Here tin and copper were the main ores exploited in the granite. To the south, in country rocks of slate, silver lead ore and copper were mined, and at Herodsfoot both lead and copper antimony ores were extracted.

The Herodsfoot Mine, in a wooded valley, is world-famous for its spectacular crystallized specimens of the mineral bournonite, a lead-antimony sulphide. The crystals often form in the shape of cog wheels, hence its other name of 'cogwheel' ore. Associated with the bournonite were well-crystallized specimens of tetrahedrite, a copper and iron-antimony sulphide which, as it name implies, forms

Clockwise from top left: Bournonite, Herodsfoot Mine, Landreath; tetrahedrite, Herodsfoot Mine; chalcosiderite, Stowes Shaft, Wheal Phoenix, Minions; cuprite, Wheal Phoenix

tetrahedron crystals, often coated by golden chalcopyrite (copper sulphide) crystals. Galena – lead sulphide – also occurred in the same mineralized veins.

Around and in the granite at Minions, near the granite tor named the Cheesewring, is the famous copper mine Wheal Phoenix. Here, during the mining for copper ore, were

West Caradon Mine from Caradon Hill

found superb crystals of copper oxide, in the form of large, dark red crystals of cuprite, and rare green, crystallized copper phosphates of chalcosiderite; blue henwoodite – a form of turquoise – and dark green libethenite. The mine encountered these secondary copper minerals near the surface, and again, interestingly, at depth, due to the intersection with a cross-course or cross-cutting structure carrying oxygenated waters. The Caradon Mine near Caradon Hill produced some of the finest dark blue azurite specimens in the county; nearby, at Marke Valley Mine, the white mineral liskeardite was first discovered, and named after the town of Liskeard. This mineral was often associated with other very colourful copper arsenates.

To the south, in country rocks of slate at Wheal Wrey, superb specimens of well-crystallized calcite used to be found. At Wheal Mary Ann, at Menheniot, just south-east of Liskeard, cubes of well-crystallized fluorite in

Clockwise from top left: Henwoodite, Wheal Phoenix, Minions; azurite, South Caradon Mine; calcite, Wheal Wrey; liskeardite, Marke Valley Mine

shades of white to yellow occurred. Many of these are now in museums. Pseudomorphs of quartz after fluorite also occurred, as well as the mineral barite, a barium sulphate. Ruby silver minerals, and occasional native silver, have occurred in mines such as Wheal Ludcott around St Ive, as here the lead sulphide mineral galena is very rich in silver.

East Cornwall: Callington to Calstock

Dominated by the granite hill known as Kit Hill, with the stack of South Kit Hill Mine on the summit to the west at Callington, the district of East Cornwall extends to the wooded incised valley and estuary of the River Tamar at Calstock, with the railway viaduct crossing the river from Devon. Granite outcrops at Kit Hill, and further on at Hingston Down. The area has been most productive for tin and copper, with tungsten around the granite, but silver-bearing lead, with native silver from Wheal Duchy near Calstock, and especially Wheal Brothers just east of Callington, was also an important ore. Additionally, the area is famous for the production of arsenic for insecticide. At one time the district, incorporating the Devonshire side, produced up to 50 per cent of the world's arsenic.

At Wheal Brothers, the following minerals were discovered: native silver, the ruby silver pyrargyrite; silver sulphide acanthite; lead sulphide galena, and iron carbonate siderite. Mine dumps, old engine houses and stacks are still greatly in evidence over much of the area. At Kit Hill, mineralized veins were

important for the tin ore cassiterite, as well as wolframite, an ore of tungsten. Further east, towards Gunnislake, tin and copper were important ores, but Old Gunnislake Mine produced the green, secondary uranium mineral metatorbernite in superb, well-crystallized specimens, as well as the dark green secondary copper phosphate mineral libethenite. Above, at Hingston Down Mine, the apple-green mineral arthurite was once abundant on the old spoil tips. This is the type locality for this rare mineral. Much of that side of Hingston Down is now occupied by a quarry for road stone. Here, molybdenite (molybdenum sulphide) – a soft, silver-coloured mineral – as well as tungsten minerals such as wolframite and scheelite – a creamy-coloured calcium tungstate mineral – are found. Occurring occasionally with the wolframite is the rare, yellow-orange secondary mineral, ferritungstite. With these minerals, occurring in abundance, is the silvery-coloured arsenopyrite, an arsenic mineral. Many other, and sometimes rare to very rare, minerals have been recorded, and occasional cubes

Kit Hill (top); Calstock (above)

Clockwise from top left: Metatorbernite, Old Gunnislake Mine, Gunnislake; libethenite, Old Gunnislake Mine; molybdenite, Hingston Down, near Gunnislake; arthurite, Hingston Down

of green fluorite were found in some of the mineralized veins outcropping in the quarry.

In the deeply wooded valley below, on the Tamar near Gunnislake, at Clitters Mine, blue azurite associated with tetrahedrite was found. But this may be of 'foreign' origin, as it was in sacks, now rotted away under leaf litter. Further upstream, inland at Greystones

Clockwise from top left: Ferritungstite around wolframite, Hingston Down, near Gunnislake; fluorite, Hingston Down; rhodonite, Greystones Quarry, Lezant; aurichalcite, Greystones Quarry

Quarry, in volcanic rocks, a silver lead vein, once worked by Greystones Silver Lead Mine, was exposed by quarrying operations. This carried not only galena and rare, highly coloured secondary lead and zinc minerals, but also exposed manganese mineralization in the form of the red manganese silicate mineral rhodonite, a product of past volcanic activity.

Rocks of Cornwall

Granite, Beragh Tor, near Minions, Bodmin Moor (left). Granite, coarse- and fine-grained, St Michael's Mount causeway (right)

It is impossible to give a comprehensive account of all the rock types here. Throughout Cornwall a variety of building stone was used in the past, giving villages and stone hedges their distinctive character. Other stones have been used for road stone, decoration and the manufacture of ornamental objects, or, when decomposed into clay, become a major source of revenue for the county. Other rocks included here are either geologically interesting, or just colourful.

Throughout Cornwall, the 'backbone' running the full length from Hingston Down to Land's End, and out to the Isles of Scilly, is of the igneous rock granite. Most is concealed, but where it emerges it forms the topographic highs of moorland, with occasional impressive outcrops or tors and, at the coast, white castellated cliffs. The three main mineral constituents of granite are quartz, mica and feldspar. It can vary in texture from coarse- to fine-grained. Historically,

Pegmatites and aplites, Tremearne Cliff, near Porthleven, and pegmatite outcrop under country rocks, Tremearne Cliff (top). Praa Sands Beach, Mount's Bay, and elvan dyke, Praa Sands (above)

granite was quarried for dimension stone, with Lamorna Cove supplying stone for London Bridge. Now it is mostly quarried for road stone or for building facings.

Other hard granitic rocks are pegmatites and aplites. Pegmatites have large crystals of feldspar and quartz; aplites have small crystals. These rocks have been little used.

Near St Austell: tourmalinite, Roche Rock, Roche (left and top right). Luxullianite, Luxulyan (above)

A rock known locally as 'elvan' (technically a rhyolite) occurs as sheets or dykes in the country rock, and has occasionally been used as a building stone.

Where the granite has been altered by hydrothermal activity to form a rock composed of black tourmaline and quartz, it is known as a tourmalinite. This rock type is very resistant to weathering, so it stands out from the landscape and can form a dramatic and picturesque part of the scenery, as at Roche Rock, where it is topped by a hermitage built from the same stone. Other hydrothermal alteration of the granite has formed a very attractive decorative stone known as luxullianite, which has pink feldspars in a ground mass of black tourmaline and quartz. Sadly, this is no longer quarried.

Where the feldspar of the granite has been decomposed into kaolin, large deposits of

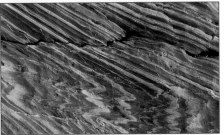

China clay pit and kaolinised granite, St Austell (above). Fine-grained turbitite sediments, Porthleven (right). Sandy sediments, St Agnes (bottom)

china clay have formed, as in the St Austell area. These deposits are of international importance, and open-pit mining has produced some very large excavations. It was in Cornwall that the first deposits of kaolin to be discovered in Europe were found by William Cookworthy, in 1746 on Tregonning Hill.

As for the older rocks in which the granite has been emplaced, most are formed from marine sediments, which are mainly fine-grained. They may also contain sandy sediments, as are exposed at Godrevy. Associated with these sedimentary rocks are volcanic rocks of basaltic origin, which erupted

Clockwise from top left: Greenstone, St Ives; Delabole Slate Quarry; Delabole slate

under the sea and are known as greenstones. Where these rocks are close to the granite, they have been metamorphosed – baked by the heat and contorted by pressure. Some fine-grained sediments, when subjected to pressure, have formed slates, as at Delabole where their fissile properties are exploited for roofing slate and decorative qualities. Other slate-like rocks in the area have been quarried for building or hedging stone.

On the Lizard peninsula, the rocks are strangely different from others in Cornwall, as they have been thrust up from deep volcanic oceanic crust. One of the oldest rocks in the county is the gneiss from the Man o' War rocks just off Lizard Head. This is an old granitic rock, which has been squeezed and contorted so that little to nothing remains of its original fabric. On the same peninsula are very dark igneous rocks like peridotite and gabbro. The gabbro has been quarried for road stone and rock armour for sea defences. There are also highly coloured rocks like the rare red and white troctolite at Coverack, and

Gneiss locality and gneiss rock, Lizard Head (top). Peridotite, Kennack Sands, the Lizard (above)

the beautifully multi-coloured rock serpentine, which is formed by hydrothermal activity passing through peridotite, and known geologically as serpentinite. Highly coloured red and green varieties of serpentine have been used for ornamental purposes, often turned on a lathe and polished, for ornaments. Turning and polishing of serpentine was a substantial industry in Victorian times, and can still be seen on the Lizard today.

The Lizard: gabbro, Coverack (top); troctolite, Coverack (mid); periodotite and serpentine, Kennack Sands

Precious Metals and Semi-precious Stones

Little has been written about Cornwall's precious metals and semi-precious stones. Gold occurs in small quantities all over the county, and is more widespread than you would think. Gold always attracts people's attention, and gold fever really happens when they first see the glistening golden grains and flakes. Most of the streams in the county carry minute traces of gold, but some are richer than others. Gold is carried in trace amounts in the mineral lodes in both chalcopyrite and pyrite, and when these break down by weathering and are transported by water, the very heavy minute gold grains are concentrated in the bottom of the valleys in the alluvium.

One of the richest rivers runs through the Ladock Valley, where tin streamers mining alluvial tin recovered substantial amounts of gold for Cornwall. The largest nugget found in the county, some 55 x 15 mm, came from

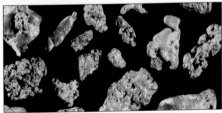

Panning for gold in a Cornish stream (top).
Gold, Ladock Valley, near Truro (right)

Native silver, Wheal Herland, Gwinear (top).
Pegmatite veins, Tremearne, nr Porthleven (above)

Silver was by far the most important precious metal extracted in Cornwall. The rich, silver-bearing (argentiferous) lead deposits of galena were exploited extensively from the Middle Ages to the late nineteenth century. In the upper parts of the ore body, where the galena was chemically leached by acidic waters, rich pockets of native silver – often formed as wires or 'sponges' – were encountered, leading to a bonanza. Native silver has been found in mines from near Land's End to the Tamar. Where deposits occur near the sea, as at Perran Silver Mine at Perranuthnoe, miners found a rare silver chloride mineral of a soft waxy appearance, named chlorargyrite. Ruby silvers of pyrargyrite and proustite, so-called because of their ruby-red colour, were found at Wheal Ludcott at St Ive. The silver sulphide argentite is found from Wheal Darlington near Ludgvan, Penzance in the southwest to the Calstock Mines on the Devon border, and at many mines in between. Native silver fringing native copper has been found in recent times on the Lizard.

Semi-precious stones such as agate and carnelian can still be found on Cornwall's beaches, especially in Mount's Bay. Amethyst occurs in veins in parts of the county, and large garnets have been found at Botallack, near

the Carnon Valley near Truro. Gold was extracted commercially from alluvial sediments near Port Gaverne in the Wadebridge area during the First World War. It has also been found in streams around North Cornwall, near Launceston. It is still possible to recover a little gold by panning, but you need a Mines Royal Licence (from the Crown Estates) to do so.

Clockwise from top left: Amethyst, Bodmin Moor; garnets, Botallack, near St Just; opal, Gunheath Pit, St Austell; topaz, Tremearne, near Porthleven (magnified image); rock crystal quartz, Perran Iron Mine, Perranporth; turquoise, Gunheath Pit, St Austell

St Just. Opal, turquoise and smoky quartz have been uncovered by opencast mining in the St Austell clay district, and occasionally clear crystals of quartz (rock crystal) have been found in various parts of the county, notably around Tintagel. Topaz occurs in many areas in granite outcrops, often in massive form, but occasionally small, green-blue crystals have been found in cavities in pegmatites. It also occurs in veins with beryl at St Michael's Mount, and there is a massive quartz and topaz rock near Cligga Head. At Trencrom Hill, near St Ives, the British Geological Survey reported finding small, cornflower-blue sapphires, and very small red spinel rubies have been recorded in beach sands.

Mineral Gallery

This selection of common to rare minerals found in Cornwall shows the diversity of colour and crystal habits.

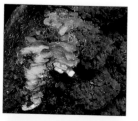

BASSETITE, Wheal Basset, Carkie, Redruth
Formula: $Fe^{2+}(UO_2)_2(PO_4)_2 \cdot 8H_2O$
Crystal habit: Monoclinic
Lustre: Vitreous
Colour: Brownish-yellow, yellow
Streak: Greenish-white
Hardness: 2½

BAYLDONITE, Penberthy Croft, St Hilary
Formula: $PbCu_3(AsO_4)_2(OH)_2$
Crystal habit: Monoclinic
Lustre: Resinous
Colour: Green, apple-green
Streak: Green
Hardness: 4½

BORNITE, Carn Brea Mine, Redruth
Formula: Cu_5FeS_4
Crystal habit: Orthorhombic (pseudo-tetragonal)
Lustre: Metallic
Colour: Copper-red, tarnishing to iridescent surface
Streak: Grey-black
Hardness: 3

BOURNONITE, Herodsfoot Mine, Landreath
Formula: $PbCuSbS_3$
Crystal habit: Orthorhombic
Lustre: Metallic
Colour: Steel-grey
Streak: Steel-grey
Hardness: $2\frac{1}{2}$–3

CASSITERITE, St Agnes
Formula: SnO_2
Crystal habit: Tetragonal
Lustre: Adamantine, greasy, sub-metallic
Colour: Black, yellow, brown, red
Streak: Brownish-white
Hardness: 6–7

CHALCOCITE, Tin Croft Mine, Camborne
Formula: Cu_2S
Crystal habit: Monoclinic
Lustre: Metallic
Colour: Blue-black, black-grey, steel-grey
Streak: Blackish lead-grey
Hardness: $2\frac{1}{2}$–3

CLINOCLASE, Wheal Gorland, St Day
Formula: $Cu^{2+}_3(AsO_4)(OH)_3$
Crystal habit: Monoclinic
Lustre: Vitreous, pearly
Colour: Blue, greenish-blue
Streak: Bluish-green
Hardness: $2\frac{1}{2}$–3

CUPRITE, Wheal Phoenix, Linkinhorne
Formula: Cu_2O
Crystal habit: Cubic
Lustre: Adamantine, sub-metallic to earthy
Colour: Dark red to cochineal red
Streak: Shining metallic brownish-red
Hardness: $3\frac{1}{2}$–4

CUPRITE, Wheal Gorland, St Day
Formula: Cu_2O
Crystal habit: Cubic
Lustre: Adamantine, sub-metallic to earthy
Colour: Dark red to cochineal red
Streak: Shining metallic brownish-red
Hardness: $3\frac{1}{2}$–4

FLUORITE, Caradon Mine, St Cleer
Formula: CaF_2
Crystal habit: Cubic
Lustre: Vitreous, dull
Colour: Purple, yellow, green, brown, colourless
Streak: White
Hardness: 4

TURQUOISE (var. Henwoodite), Wheal Phoenix, Linkinhorne
Formula: $Cu^{2+}Al_6(PO_4)_4(OH)_8 \bullet 4H_2O$
Crystal habit: Triclinic
Lustre: Vitreous, waxy, dull
Colour: Bright blue, sky-blue, green, turquoise-blue
Streak: Pale greenish-blue to white
Hardness: 5–6

LANGITE, Tresavean Mine, Lanner
Formula: $Cu_4SO_4(OH)_6 \cdot 2H_2O$
Crystal habit: Monoclinic
Lustre: Vitreous, silky
Colour: Bright blue, sky-blue, green, turquoise-blue
Streak: Pale greenish-blue to white
Hardness: 2½–3

LINARITE, Penberthy Croft, St Hilary
Formula: $PbCu^{2+}(SO_4)(OH)_2$
Crystal habit: Monoclinic
Lustre: Sub-adamantine
Colour: Deep azure-blue
Streak: Pale blue
Hardness: 2½

LIROCONITE, Wheal Gorland, St Day
Formula: $Cu^{2+}_2Al(AsO_4)(OH)_4 \cdot 4H_2O$
Crystal habit: Monoclinic
Lustre: Vitreous
Colour: Sky-blue to green
Streak: Light blue
Hardness: 2–2½

MIMETITE, Wheal Unity, St Day
Formula: $Pb_5(AsO_4)_3Cl$
Crystal habit: Hexagonal
Lustre: Sub-adamantine
Colour: Pale-yellow, yellowish-brown to orangey-red
Streak: White
Hardness: 3½–4

BISMUTH, St Ives Consols, St Ives
Formula: Bi
Crystal habit: Trigonal
Lustre: Metallic
Colour: Reddish-white to creamy-white
Streak: Silver-white
Hardness: 2–2½

COPPER, Botallack Mine, St Just
Formula: Cu
Crystal habit: Cubic
Lustre: Metallic
Colour: Copper-red
Streak: Copper-red
Hardness: 2½–3

PSEUDOMALACHITE with libethenite, South Wheal Francis, Redruth
Formula: $Cu^{2+}_{5}(PO_4)_2(OH)_4$
Crystal habit: Monoclinic
Lustre: Vitreous
Colour: Blue-green, green to dark green
Streak: Blue-green
Hardness: 4–4½

SCORODITE, Wheal Gorland, St Day
Formula: $Fe^{3+}AsO_4 \cdot 2H_2O$
Crystal habit: Orthorhombic
Lustre: Sub-adamantine, vitreous, resinous
Colour: Green, blue-grey, blue, yellow-brown
Streak: Greenish-white
Hardness: 3½–4

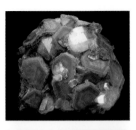

SIDERITE, Wheal Maudlin, Lanivery
Formula: $Fe^{2+}CO_3$
Crystal habit: Trigonal
Lustre: Vitreous, silky, pearly
Colour: Various shades of brown, yellow brown
Streak: White
Hardness: $3\frac{1}{2}$–$4\frac{1}{2}$

CASSITERITE, Wheal Kitty, St Agnes
Formula: SnO_2
Crystal habit: Tetragonal
Lustre: Adamantine, greasy, sub-metallic
Colour: Black, yellow, brown, red
Streak: Pale green–bluish-green
Hardness: 2

METATORBERNITE, Cornwall
Formula: $Cu^{2+}(UO_2)_2(PO_4)_2 \bullet 8H_2O$
Crystal habit: Tetragonal
Lustre: Adamantine
Colour: Bright to dark green
Streak: Light green
Hardness: $3\frac{1}{2}$–4

FLUORITE, Carn Brea Mine, Redruth
Formula: CaF_2
Crystal habit: Cubic
Lustre: Vitreous, dull
Colour: Purple, yellow, green, brown, colourless
Streak: White
Hardness: 4

TENNANTITE, Wheal Jewel, St Day
Formula: $Cu_6Cu_4(Fe,Zn)_2(As,Sb)_4S_{13}$
Crystal habit: Cubic
Lustre: Metallic
Colour: Grey-black, grey, iron-grey, black
Streak: Reddish-grey, black, red-brown
Hardness: 3–4½

GALENA (after pyromorphite), Wheal Hope, Perranzabuloe
Formula: PbS
Crystal habit: Cubic
Lustre: Metallic, dull
Colour: Lead-grey
Streak: Pale green–bluish-green
Hardness: 2½

SCORODITE, Wheal Gorland, St Day
Formula: $Fe^{3+}AsO_4 \bullet 2H_2O$
Crystal habit: Orthorhombic
Lustre: Sub-adamantine, vitreous, resinous
Colour: Green, blue-grey, blue, yellow-brown
Streak: Greenish-white
Hardness: 3½– 4

OLIVENITE, Wheal Gorland, St Day
Formula: $Cu^{2+}_2(AsO_4)(OH)$
Crystal habit: Monoclinic
Lustre: Adamantine
Colour: Olive-green, yellow to grey-green
Streak: Olive-green to brown
Hardness: 3

COPPER, Wheal Gorland, St Day
Formula: Cu
Crystal habit: Cubic
Lustre: Metallic
Colour: Copper-red
Streak: Copper-red
Hardness: $2\frac{1}{2}$–3

PSEUDOMALACHITE, Phoenix Mine, Linkinhorne
Formula: $Cu^{2+}_5(PO_4)_2(OH)_4$
Crystal habit: Monoclinic
Lustre: Vitreous
Colour: Blue-green, green to dark green
Streak: Blue-green
Hardness: 4–$4\frac{1}{2}$

QUARTZ (var. Amethyst), Unity Wood Mine, St Day
Formula: SiO_2
Crystal habit: Trigonal
Lustre: Vitreous
Colour: Colourless, white, purple, black
Streak: White
Hardness: 7

WOLFRAMITE (var. Ferberite, after scheelite), Hingston Down
Formula: $(Fe^{2+})WO_4$ to $(Mn^{2+})WO_4$ Quarry, Gunnislake
Crystal habit: Monoclinic
Lustre: Sub-metallic
Colour: Greyish-black
Streak: Reddish-brown
Hardness: 4–$4\frac{1}{2}$

QUARTZ (var. Chalcedony), Trevaskis Mine, Gwinear
Formula: SiO_2
Crystal habit: Trigonal
Lustre: Vitreous
Colour: Colourless, white, purple, black
Streak: White
Hardness: 7

CALCITE, Herodsfoot Mine, Landreath
Formula: $CaCO_3$
Crystal habit: Trigonal
Lustre: Vitreous, pearly
Colour: White, yellow, red, orange ---
Streak: White
Hardness: 3

ATACAMITE, Levant Mine, Pendeen
Formula: $Cu^{2+}_2Cl(OH)_3$
Crystal habit: Orthorhombic
Lustre: Adamantine, vitreous
Colour: Bright to dark green
Streak: Apple-green
Hardness: 3–3½

OLIVENITE, Wheal Phoenix, Linkinhorne
Formula: $Cu^{2+}_2(AsO_4)(OH)$
Crystal habit: Monoclinic
Lustre: Adamantine
Colour: Olive-green, yellow to grey-green
Streak: Olive-green to brown
Hardness: 3

COPPER, Botallack Mine, St Just
Formula: Cu
Crystal habit: Cubic
Lustre: Metallic
Colour: Copper-red
Streak: Copper-red
Hardness: 2½–3

CHALCOCITE (var. Djurieite), Cook's Kitchen Mine, Camborne
Formula: $Cu_{31}S_{16}$
Crystal habit: Monoclinic
Lustre: Metallic
Colour: Blue-black, black-grey, steel-grey
Streak: Blackish lead-grey
Hardness: 2½–3

CASSITERITE, Wheal Lovel, Wendron
Formula: SnO_2
Crystal habit: Tetragonal
Lustre: Adamantine, greasy, sub-metallic
Colour: Black, yellow, brown, red
Streak: Brownish-white
Hardness: 6–7

CHALCOPYRITE (var. Blister Copper), Ale & Cakes Mine, Gwennap
Formula: $CuFeS_2$
Crystal habit: Tetragonal
Lustre: Metallic
Colour: Brass-yellow, often with iridescent tarnish
Streak: Greenish-black
Hardness: 3½–4

BARITE, Ale & Cakes Mine, Gwennap
Formula: $BaSO_4$
Crystal habit: Orthorhombic
Lustre: Vitreous, pearly
Colour: Colourless, white, yellow
Streak: White
Hardness: 3–3½

BOTALLACKITE, Levant Mine, Pendeen
Formula: $Cu^{2+}_2Cl(OH)_3$
Crystal habit: Monoclinic
Lustre: Pearly
Colour: Bluish-green to green
Streak: Light green
Hardness: Soft

CHALCOCITE, St Ives Consols, St Ives
Formula: Cu_2S
Crystal habit: Monoclinic
Lustre: Metallic
Colour: Blue-black, black-grey, steel-grey
Streak: Blackish lead-grey
Hardness: 2½–3

CHALCOCITE, St Ives Consols, St Ives
Formula: Cu_2S
Crystal habit: Monoclinic
Lustre: Metallic
Colour: Blue-black, black-grey, steel-grey
Streak: Blackish lead-grey
Hardness: 2½–3

CLINOCLASE (with blue liroconite), Wheal Gorland, St Day
Formula: $Cu^{2+}_3(AsO_4)(OH)_3$
Crystal habit: Monoclinic
Lustre: Vitreous, pearly
Colour: Blue, greenish-blue
Streak: Bluish-green
Hardness: 2½–3

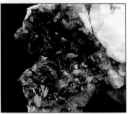

CLINOCLASE, Wheal Gorland, St Day
Formula: $Cu^{2+}_3(AsO_4)(OH)_3$
Crystal habit: Monoclinic
Lustre: Vitreous, pearly
Colour: Blue, greenish-blue
Streak: Bluish-green
Hardness: 2½–3

PHARMACOSIDERITE, Wheal Gorland, St Day
Formula: $KFe^{3+}_4(AsO_4)_3(OH)_4 \bullet 6\text{-}7H_2O$
Crystal habit: Cubic
Lustre: Adamantine, greasy
Colour: Green, emerald-green to dark brown
Streak: Yellowish-green
Hardness: 2½

CUPRITE, Wheal Phoenix, Linkinhorne
Formula: Cu_2O
Crystal habit: Cubic
Lustre: Adamantine, sub-metallic to earthy
Colour: Dark red to cochineal red
Streak: Shining metallic brownish-red
Hardness: 3½–4

ERYTHRITE, Botallack Mine, St Just
Formula: $Co_3(AsO_4)_2 \bullet 8H_2O$
Crystal habit: Monoclinic
Lustre: Dull, earthy
Colour: Crimson to peach-red, pale rose-pink
Streak: Pale red to pink
Hardness: 1½–2½

FLUORITE, Trovis Quarry, Longdowns
Formula: CaF_2
Crystal habit: Cubic
Lustre: Vitreous, dull
Colour: Purple, yellow, green, brown, colourless
Streak: White
Hardness: 4

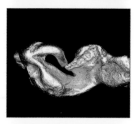

GOLD, Carnon Valley, Carnon Downs
Formula: Au
Crystal habit: Cubic
Lustre: Metallic
Colour: Rich yellow
Streak: Shining yellow
Hardness: 2½–3

HAEMATITE, Restormal Royal Mine, Lostwithiel
Formula: Fe_2O_3
Crystal habit: Trigonal
Lustre: Metallic, sub-metallic, dull, earthy
Colour: Steel-grey to bright to dull red-brown
Streak: Reddish-brown
Hardness: 5–6

CASSITERITE (pseudomorph after feldspar), Wheal Coates, St Agnes
Formula: SnO_2
Crystal habit: Tetragonal
Lustre: Adamantine, greasy, sub-metallic
Colour: Black, yellow, brown, red
Streak: Brownish-white
Hardness: 6–7

LIROCONITE, Wheal Gorland, St Day
Formula: $Cu^{2+}_2Al(AsO_4)(OH)_4 \bullet 4H_2O$
Crystal habit: Monoclinic
Lustre: Vitreous
Colour: Sky-blue to green
Streak: Light blue
Hardness: 2–2½

PYROMORPHITE, Wheal Alfred, Hayle
Formula: $Pb_5(PO_4)_3Cl$
Crystal habit: Hexagonal
Lustre: Sub-adamantine, resinous
Colour: Green, yellowish-green, brown, white, colourless
Streak: White
Hardness: 3½–4

PYROMORPHITE, Pool Mine, Helston
Formula: $Pb_5(PO_4)_3Cl$
Crystal habit: Hexagonal
Lustre: Sub-adamantine, resinous
Colour: Green, yellowish-green, brown, white, colourless
Streak: White
Hardness: 3½–4

SIDERITE on QUARTZ, Tincroft Mine, Camborne

Formula: $Fe^{2+}CO_3$
Crystal habit: Trigonal
Lustre: Vitreous, silky, pearly
Colour: Various shades of brown, yellow brown
Streak: White
Hardness: $3\frac{1}{2}-4\frac{1}{2}$

SPALERITE, Wheal Jane, Carnon Downs

Formula: ZnS
Crystal habit: Cubic
Lustre: Adamantine, resinous
Colour: Yellow, light to dark brown
Streak: Pale yellow to brown
Hardness: $3\frac{1}{2}-4$

CASSSITERITE (var. Wood tin), Wheal Kitty, St Agnes

Formula: SnO_2
Crystal habit: Tetragonal
Lustre: Adamantine, greasy, sub-metallic
Colour: Black, yellow, brown, red
Streak: Brownish-white
Hardness: 6–7

PHOSGENITE, Wheal Rose, Porthleven

Formula: $Pb_2(CO_3)Cl_2$
Crystal habit: Tetragonal
Lustre: Adamantine
Colour: Colourless, white, yellow-brown
Streak: White
Hardness: 2–3

ARSENOPYRITE, Trevaskis Mine, Gwinear
Formula: $FeAsS$
Crystal habit: Monoclinic
Lustre: Metallic
Colour: Silver-white to steel-grey
Streak: Grey-black
Hardness: $5\frac{1}{2}$–6

AXINITE- (Fe), Botallack, St Just
Formula: $Ca_2Fe^{2+}Al_2[OH.BSi_4O_{15}]$
Crystal habit: Triclinic
Lustre: Vitreous
Colour: Translucent, lilac-brown
Streak: White
Hardness: $6\frac{1}{2}$–7

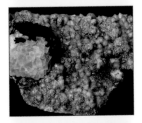

FLUORITE on AMETHYST, Wheal Jane, Carnon Downs
Formula: CaF_2
Crystal habit: Cubic
Lustre: Vitreous, dull
Colour: Purple, yellow, green, brown, colourless
Streak: White
Hardness: 4

GALENA, West Chiverton Mine, Perranzabuloe
Formula: PbS
Crystal habit: Cubic
Lustre: Metallic, dull
Colour: Lead-grey
Streak: Lead-grey
Hardness: $2\frac{1}{2}$

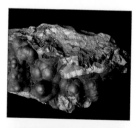

HAEMATITE, Geevor Mine, Pendeen
Formula: Fe_2O_3
Crystal habit: Trigonal
Lustre: Metallic, sub-metallic, dull, earthy
Colour: Steel-grey to black in crystals to red when massive
Streak: Reddish-brown
Hardness: 5–6

CHALCOPYRITE on FLUORITE, Tincroft Mine, Camborne
Formula: CaF_2
Crystal habit: Cubic
Lustre: Vitreous, dull
Colour: Purple, yellow, green, brown, colourless
Streak: White
Hardness: 4

CRONSTEDITE, Wheal Jane Mine, Carnon Downs
Formula: $Fe^{2+}_2Fe^{3+}(Si,Fe^{3+})O_5(OH)_4$
Crystal habit: Monoclinic and trigonal
Lustre: Vitreous
Colour: Black, dark brown-black
Streak: Dark olive-green
Hardness: $3\frac{1}{2}$

GALENA, Silver Vein Mine, Lostwithiel
Formula: PbS
Crystal habit: Cubic
Lustre: Metallic, dull
Colour: Lead-grey
Streak: Lead-grey
Hardness: $2\frac{1}{2}$

QUARTZ, Clay Pits, St Austell
Formula: SiO_2
Crystal habit: Trigonal
Lustre: Vitreous
Colour: Colourless, white, purple, black
Streak: White
Hardness: 7

FLUORITE, Wheal Mary Ann, Menheniot
Formula: CaF_2
Crystal habit: Cubic
Lustre: Vitreous, dull
Colour: Purple, yellow, green, brown, colourless
Streak: White
Hardness: 4

CASITERITE (var. Wood tin), Garth Mine, nr. Penzance
Formula: SnO_2
Crystal habit: Tetragonal
Lustre: Adamantine, greasy, sub-metallic
Colour: Black, yellow, brown, red
Streak: Brownish-white
Hardness: 6–7

QUARTZ, Wheal Edward, St Just
Formula: SiO_2
Crystal habit: Trigonal
Lustre: Vitreous
Colour: Colourless, white, purple, black
Streak: White
Hardness: 7

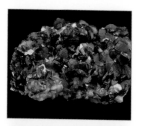

SIDERITE on QUARTZ, Tincroft Mine, Camborne
Formula: $Fe^{2+}CO_3$
Crystal habit: Trigonal
Lustre: Vitreous, silky, pearly
Colour: Various shades of brown, yellow brown
Streak: White
Hardness: $3\frac{1}{2}$–$4\frac{1}{2}$

TERAHEDRITE, Herodsfoot Mine, Landreath
Formula: $Cu_6Cu_4(Fe,Zn)_2(Sb,As)_4S_{13}$
Crystal habit: Cubic
Lustre: Metallic
Colour: Steel to iron-grey
Streak: Black, brown to dark red
Hardness: $3\frac{1}{2}$–4

PYRITE, Wheal Jane Mine, Carnon Downs
Formula: FeS_2
Crystal habit: Cubic
Lustre: Metallic
Colour: Pale brass-yellow
Streak: Greenish-black
Hardness: 6–$6\frac{1}{2}$

AZURITE, South Caradon Mine
Formula: $Cu^{2+}_3(CO_3)_2(OH)_2$
Crystal habit: Monoclinic
Lustre: Vitreous
Colour: Azure-blue, blue, light blue, or dark blue
Streak: Light blue
Hardness: $3\frac{1}{2}$–4

CHALCOPHYLLITE, Wheal Gorland, St Day
Formula: $Cu_2Al(AsO_4)_2(SO_4)_{1.5}(OH)_{12} \cdot 18H_2O$
Crystal habit: Trigonal
Lustre: Sub-adamantine, vitreous, pearly
Colour: Emerald-green, grass-green
Streak: Pale green to bluish-green
Hardness: 2

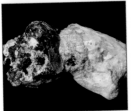

CLINOCLASE, Wheal Gorland, St Day
Formula: $Cu^{2+}_3(AsO_4)(OH)_3$
Crystal habit: Monoclinic
Lustre: Vitreous, pearly
Colour: Blue, greenish-blue
Streak: Bluish-green
Hardness: 2½–3

LANGITE, Fowey Consols, Tywardreath
Formula: $Cu_4^{2+}(SO_4)(OH)_6 \cdot 2H_2O$
Crystal habit: Monoclinic
Lustre: Vitreous, silky
Colour: Blue, greenish-blue to white
Streak: Greenish-blue
Hardness: 2½–3

PYROMORPHITE, Penberthy Croft, St Hilary
Formula: $Pb_5(PO_4)_3Cl$
Crystal habit: Hexagonal
Lustre: Sub-adamantine, resinous
Colour: Green, yellowish-green, brown, white, colourless
Streak: White
Hardness: 3½–4

OTHOCLASE FELDSPAR, Tremearne, nr. Porthleven
Formula: $KAlSi_3O_8$
Crystal habit: Monoclinic
Lustre: Vitreous
Colour: Greyish-yellow, white, pink
Streak: White
Hardness: 6

WOLFRAMITE, East Pool Mine, Camborne
Formula: $(Mn,Fe)WO_4$
Crystal habit: Monoclinic
Lustre: Sub-metallic
Colour: Greyish-black
Streak: Reddish-brown
Hardness: $4-4\frac{1}{2}$

CUPRITE (var. Chalcotrichite), Wheal Phoenix, Linkinhorne
Formula: Cu_2O
Crystal habit: Cubic
Lustre: Adamantine, sub-metallic to earthy
Colour: Dark red to cochineal red
Streak: Shining metallic brownish-red
Hardness: $3\frac{1}{2}-4$

CONNELLITE with botallackite, Levant Mine, Pendeen
Formula: $Cu^{2+}_{19}Cl_4(SO_4)(OH)_{32} \cdot 3H_2O$
Crystal habit: Hexagonal
Lustre: Vitreous
Colour: Blue, blue-green
Streak: Pale green-blue
Hardness: 3

CERULEITE, Wheal Gorland, St Day
Formula: $Cu_2Al_7(AsO_4)_4(OH)_{13} \bullet 12H_2O$
Crystal habit: Triclinic
Lustre: —
Colour: Turquoise-blue
Streak: Bluish-white
Hardness: 5–6

MALACHITE, United Mines, Gwennap
Formula: $Cu^{2+}_2(CO_3)_2(OH)_2$
Crystal habit: Monoclinic
Lustre: Adamantine, vitreous, silky, dull, earthy
Colour: Green
Streak: Light green
Hardness: 3½–4

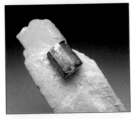

FLUORAPATITE on FELDSPAR , Chywoon Quarry, Longdowns
Formula: $Ca_5(PO_4)_3(F)$
Crystal habit: Hexagonal
Lustre: Vitreous
Colour: Colourless, white, green, blue, yellow, brown, violet, purple
Streak: White
Hardness: 5

GOETHITE, Restormal Royal Mine, Lostwithiel
Formula: : $Fe^{3+}O(OH)$
Crystal habit: Orthorhombic
Lustre: Adamantine, silky, metallic, dull
Colour: Brownish-black, yellow-brown, reddish-brown
Streak: Yellowish-brown, orange-yellow, ochre-yellow
Hardness: 5–5½

Glossary

batholith: a large emplacement of igneous intrusive rock

dimension stone: a natural stone that has been cut or trimmed, mainly for building work

dyke: a sheet-like intrusion

fissile: rock tends to break along sheet-like planes

gossan: intensely oxidized, weathered or decomposed rock, usually the upper and exposed part of an ore deposit or mineral vein where all that remains are iron oxides and quartz

hydrothermal: the circulation of hot water often associated with igneous intrusions

igneous rock: formed by magma (molten rock) being cooled and becoming solid

lithosphere: the rigid outermost shell of a rocky planet

mantle: a lower layer in the interior of the earth, below the crust composed of ultra-mafic (see **ultrabasic** below) rocks

metalliferous: metal-bearing; often hydro-thermal waters carry metals in solution

metamorphic aureole: that area of rock altered by contact with an igneous intrusion

metamorphic rock: the result of the trans-formation of an existing rock type, in a process called metamorphism, by heat and pressure causing recrystalization

mine sett: the land that is the subject of the mine lease covering the extraction of mineral(s)

mineralization: the hydrothermal deposi-tion of economically important metals in the formation of ore bodies or 'lodes'

ophiolite: a section of the earth's oceanic crust and the underlying rocks (mantle) that has been uplifted or emplaced to be exposed within rocks at the earth's crust

orogeny: natural mountain-building occur-ring during the process of plate tectonics

placer mining: the mining of alluvial – usually water-borne – deposits for minerals

plate tectonics: the large-scale motions of the earth's lithosphere

pseudomorph: where one mineral is re-placed by another, but keeps the crystal habit of the former